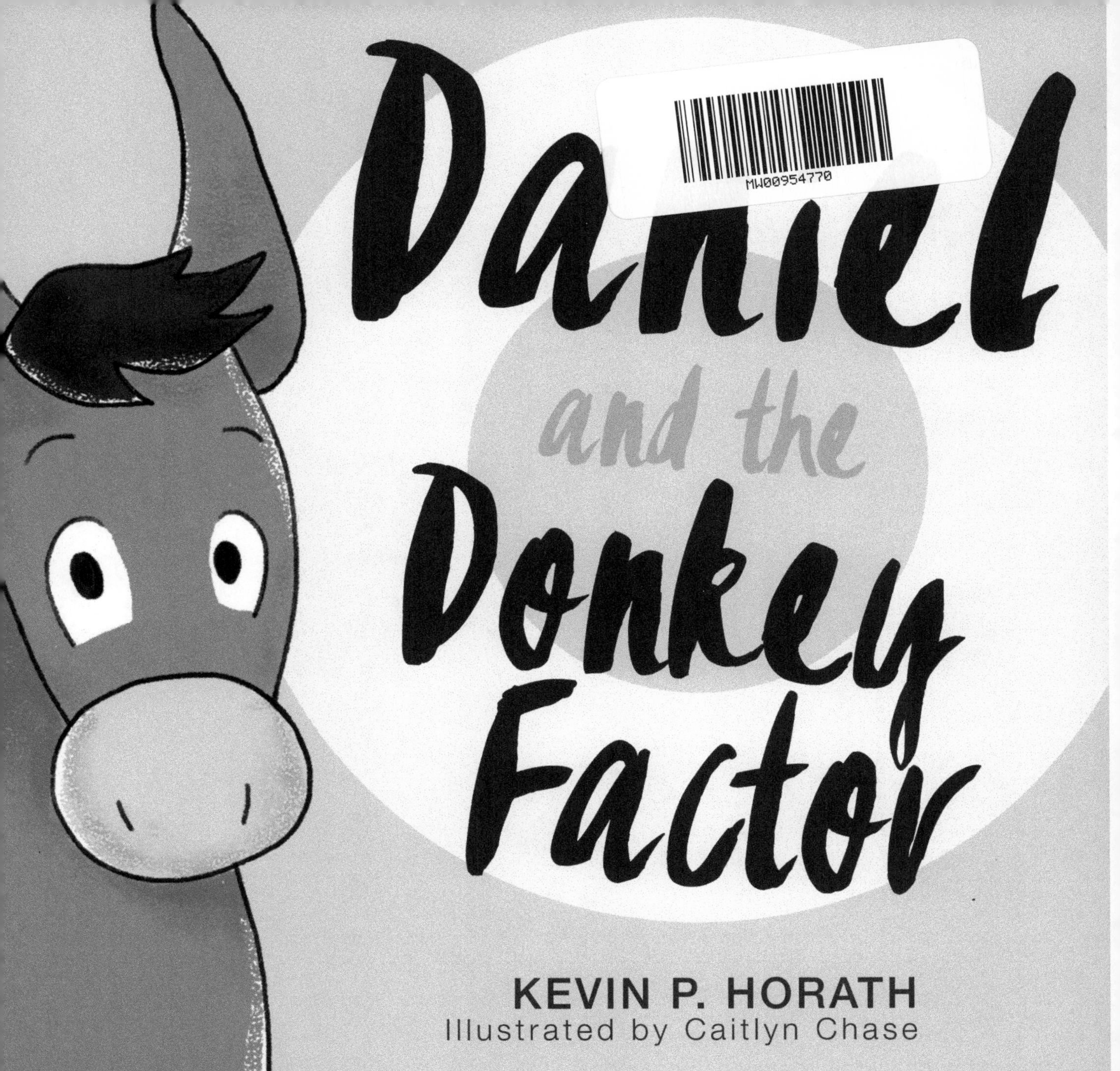
MW00954770
Daniel
and the
Donkey
Factor
KEVIN P. HORATH
Illustrated by Caitlyn Chase
LUCIDBOOKS

Daniel and the Donkey Factor

Illustrations by Caitlyn Chase
Published by Lucid Books in Houston, TX
www.LucidBooksPublishing.com

ISBN-10: 1-63296-254-3
ISBN-13: 978-1-63296-254-6
eISBN-10: 1-63296-275-6
eISBN-13: 978-1-63296-275-1

Special Sales: Most Lucid Books titles are available in special quantity discounts. Custom imprinting or excerpting can also be done to fit special needs. Contact Lucid Books at info@lucidbookspublishing.com.

For Norah, Penelope, and Henry

Long ago, outside the city of Jerusalem, a baby donkey was born. All the barn animals gathered to welcome this new arrival.

An owl asked from the rafters, "Whoo . . . whoo is this?"

"This," the donkey's father answered, "is Daniel."

As Daniel grew, he played with the other young animals in the barn.

One day as they went out to the yard together, the animals made fun of him.

"Donkeys sound funny," said the owlet.

The calf said, "They are dirty, too. Donkeys are unclean."

The colt replied, "Warriors ride horses because horses are better in battle."

"Yeah, what good are donkeys?" they all laughed together.

Joshua the lamb stood close by. "Please stop, everybody," he pleaded. "You are not being very nice."

So the animals started to tease Joshua too!

Daniel decided to sneak away. He was sad because his friends had hurt his feelings.

Back inside the barn, Daniel's parents could tell something was wrong. "Why are you so sad?" Daniel's mother asked.

Daniel replied, "Is it true that donkeys are unclean? Why are horses better in battle? Why does everyone, except Joshua, make fun of me?"

"Oh, Daniel," his mother said. "Let me tell you a story. Many years ago, God made everything and all of us to be different. We just have to find that special way we are to serve God.

"Donkeys are considered unclean under God's Law," she continued. "Yet He loves us so much that He made a way for us to serve Him. Did you know that prophets, priests, and kings ride donkeys? Donkeys carry very important people!"

"Really?" Daniel wondered. "But we sound so funny."

"Hee-haw," Daniel's father brayed. "Yes, Daniel, we do. But God once used a donkey to speak to a prophet. God can use anyone, Daniel. He can use you."

"How?" Daniel asked.

"One day, you will know. Until then, we will teach you and show you the way," his mother lovingly replied.

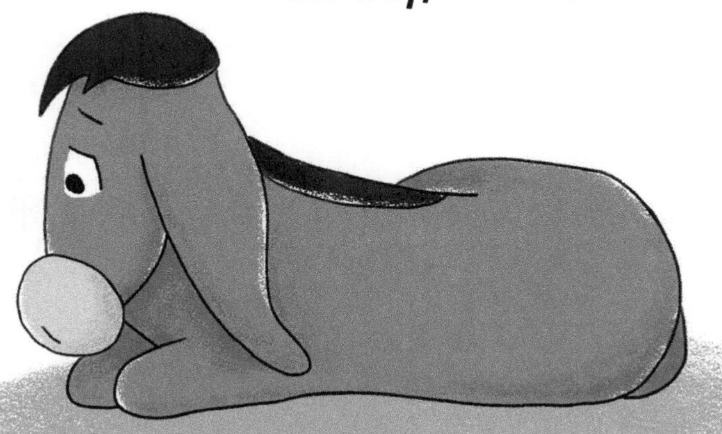

And they both did just that. Daniel learned as he grew big and strong.

Months later, many people came to Jerusalem to celebrate a holiday called Passover. Daniel and his mother heard they were going into the city with their owner to get food for the party. While they waited outside the barn, two strange men appeared. They told Daniel's owner that the Lord needed to use Daniel and his mother.

This frightened Daniel. He did not know these men or what they would do. "Hee-haw, hee-haw!" Daniel brayed in fear.

His mother said, "Daniel, do not be afraid. These men are with a special man who teaches about God. He is kind to animals, children, and all people. I know we can trust them. Follow me." So Daniel bravely followed his mother.

Suddenly, a different man appeared. This man gently reached up and scratched Daniel behind his ears. He lowered His head and hugged Daniel's neck. Daniel was no longer afraid. He looked up and saw his mother looking at him. She gently nodded as the man sat on Daniel.

The other men led Daniel's mother toward the city. Daniel followed with the man riding on his back.

Jerusalem was crowded! People were all around. Some of them took off their coats and laid them in the path. Other people grabbed palm branches and spread them along the path. Daniel heard, "Hosanna to the Son of David: blessed is He who comes in the name of the Lord! Hosanna in the highest!"

Daniel's father had once told him of a king named David. "If this is the Son of David, He must be royalty, too," Daniel thought. Maybe a king was riding Daniel! He took every step carefully.

On the way to the temple, Daniel learned the man's name. "Look, it's the prophet," he heard the people say. "It is Jesus!"

Later that night, Daniel was so excited. He told the story over and over to the amazement of his friends. This time they did not tease him. They listened to every word. After talking for what seemed like hours, Daniel fell asleep and dreamed about his exciting day.

Several days later, Daniel and his mother returned to the city. Maybe Daniel would get to see Jesus again!

As they got close, Daniel noticed a change. Something was wrong! On a scary-looking hill were three crosses. Daniel heard some people talking. Some were crying. Some were even yelling. Soldiers were everywhere. Jesus, who had ridden Daniel just a few days ago, was on the middle cross. Daniel did not understand.

The sun began to set. Daniel realized he was walking through the shadow of the cross from high up on the hill. Tears came to his eyes. He was sad.

As Daniel followed his mother home, he noticed the shape of a cross on her back. Was it the shadow? No, it wasn't. As they got farther and farther away, the cross remained on her back.

Back home in the barn, Daniel asked, "Why were people mean to Jesus?"

Daniel's mother replied, "Remember when I told you that God provided a way for the donkey to serve Him?"

"Yes," Daniel answered. "I will always remember that story."

"Good. Now I will tell you a little more. Joshua the lamb stood up for you when your friends teased you. That is like what God did for donkeys. Because we are unclean, He allowed for a lamb to take our place.

"Today, you saw the very same thing happen for people," she continued. "They disobeyed God, so now they are unclean. Still, He loves them so much that He made a way for them to serve Him, too. Jesus is their Lamb. And you, Daniel, carried Him: the Prophet, Priest, and King."

Amazed, Daniel replied, "As we left, I noticed the shape of the cross is on your back. Why is that?"

Daniel's mother laughed and said, "It is on your back too, Daniel. All donkeys have the shape of the cross. We carry the Word of God. The cross reminds us of that job."

And so Daniel thought about all these things.

About forty days later, Daniel, along with his parents, returned to Jerusalem. They went up a hill called the Mount of Olives. There were people there, including some men he had seen before. Daniel thought, "They were with Jesus!" He was excited. Could it be possible? Yes, Jesus was there, too!

Jesus walked over to Daniel. He gently scratched Daniel behind his ears.

Jesus then lowered His head and hugged Daniel's neck for just a moment.

Jesus stood up and gave Daniel a wink and a nod. Turning to Daniel's mother, He patted her gently on the neck, whispering "Thank you" in her ear.

Suddenly, Jesus began to rise to heaven. As He did, He said, "Go and teach everyone the things I have taught you. Remember, I am always with you." And just like that, Jesus was gone.

Daniel had learned his purpose. Life was not always easy. But he never forgot the lessons his parents had taught him, especially the memory of his mother leading him to Jesus.

Daniel knew he had carried the King of kings, and now he carried the message of the cross. He knew that was a big job—a job meant for a donkey.

That was the donkey factor.

And you know what?

It is your job, too. Now you can go out and find your own special way to serve God and carry the message of the cross—just like Daniel did.

THE END

About the Illustrator

Caitlyn Chase is a 2018 graduate of the animation program at Huntington University in Huntington, Indiana. She specializes in 2-D work (animating, drawing, illustrating) and is currently working as a graphic designer while illustrating her first book. For her future, Caitlyn imagines herself with her husband, surrounded by dogs and books while pursuing a career that helps bring stories to life.

About the Author

Kevin P. Horath, author of *The Elisha Factor* and *The Pharaoh Factor*, is a dynamic speaker and teacher who has served as Associate Pastor for Hillside Bethel Tabernacle since 1997 and worked as a healthcare human resources executive for over 27 years. He holds a bachelor of science in management from the University of Illinois at Springfield. Kevin lives in Decatur, Illinois, with his wife, Kathy. They have three children, three grandchildren, two dogs, and one cat. In their free time, Kevin and Kathy love to sail on Lake Decatur. His goal is to help others find a spiritually healthy approach to life through the realistic, practical application of biblical stories, characters, and principles. Follow along with Kevin's work at www.thefactorbooks.com!

CPSIA information can be obtained
at www.ICGtesting.com
Printed in the USA
BVHW022143060322
630775BV00002B/4